VIKING STORIES

VIKING STORIES

Collected and illustrated
by
Davy Cooper

Shetland Amenity Trust
Lerwick
2004

Viking Stories

© Shetland Amenity Trust, 2004.

Illustrations © Davy Cooper, 2004.

ISBN 0 9543246 1 7

First published by Shetland Amenity Trust, 2004.

Printed by
Shetland Litho,
Gremista, Lerwick,
Shetland ZE1 0PX.

CONTENTS

Introduction 3

The Giant's Grave 6

Pettawater 11

The Raven's Revenge 14

The Beacon 18

Herma and Saxa 27

The Sea King 30

The Hooded Man 37

The Bear 40

Yela Brun 46

Geitishamrar 51

Voyage of the Dratsie 59

INTRODUCTION

This book is a small collection of stories involving Shetland which may or may not trace their origins back to Viking times. It isn't oral history and it doesn't try to give any great insight into the mind, customs and cultures of the Norse settlers in Shetland. I say this up front because I don't want any potential reader to get the wrong impression. What you have in your hands is a collection of stories which have been handed down over the years and have been told around Shetland fire sides for many generations. In most cases it is almost impossible to trace their origins or even to establish if they do indeed stretch back into the distant past. They are entertainments designed in many cases to offer an explanation of a place name or to indicate the origins of a particular geographical feature and in this they share a common thread with folk tales the world over. As such the relative amount of truth and fiction involved is very much open to question and I would suggest that the reader should regard them as largely fictional and simply enjoy them for what they are.

Place names are a key element to many of these stories and to this end I have included a map that pinpoints many of the names mentioned. Some of these are speculative since the names themselves have been corrupted or have disappeared over time. It may please the reader however to be able to visit some of the sites mentioned and picture the events as they unfold in the actual landscape.

Shetland has always had a strong oral tradition of storytelling and as compiler of this little collection I would be remiss if I did not acknowledge those who have kept that tradition alive. These stories have spawned as many versions as there are storytellers to tell them but I feel I must mention one or two masters of the craft who have been a major inspiration for this work. No one dealing with Viking stories can or should ignore the works of Andrew T Cluness whose "Told Around the Peat Fire" includes many of the best examples, particularly those based in Unst. (None of the stories in this collection are direct copies of work published elsewhere but a list of recommended further reading is included at the back of this book.) Likewise there is a need to recognise the contributions of James J (Jamsie) Laurenson from Fetlar, a man of considerable talents in many fields whose stories are deserving of more frequent and dare I say it more prestigious publication than has been the case up until now.

The work of the celebrated Orkney historian, writer and broadcaster Ernest W Marwick has also been most useful in my researches and his "The Folklore of Orkney and Shetland" is still regarded by many as one of the best works in the field. Finally I must acknowledge the contribution of those Icelandic saga poets of the distant past who provided the stories from the Orkneyinga and Fljotsdala sagas. Would that I could name them but unfortunately all that I can do is salute their efforts and commend the sagas to the reader as one of the greatest collections of early literature ever to be produced by a single culture.

I am not a great believer in long introductions so I will leave the reader at this point to their own devices. I hope this little book may whet the appetite and send them on a journey of discovery into the world of stories and sagas. I also hope that the reader finds this journey as enjoyable as I have.

Davy Cooper

SHETLAND ISLANDS

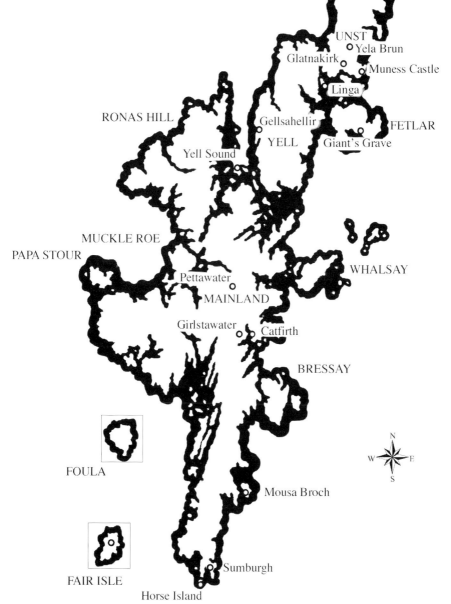

Burrafirth
Hermaness
Saxavord

UNST
Yela Brun
Glatnakirk
Muness Castle

Linga

RONAS HILL

Gellsahellir
FETLAR
YELL
Giant's Grave
Yell Sound

MUCKLE ROE

PAPA STOUR
WHALSAY

Pettawater
MAINLAND

Girlstawater
Catfirth

BRESSAY

N
W E
S

FOULA

Mousa Broch

FAIR ISLE

Sumburgh

Horse Island

THE GIANT'S GRAVE

It must have been a fine morning, one of those clear winter days when the sun shines and the sea is like a mirror among the fjords. Otherwise he would never have risked going to the fishing in a 13-foot boat, especially after a week of storms. Either that or hunger was gnawing at his belly and that of his family. No weather forecasts in those days to consult or ponder over, just the experience of a lifetime lived on the sea and the knowledge of generations passed from father to son. He must have known the risks and weighed them up against the rewards. Whatever the reason he set out from his home on the coast of Norway to try for fish. No one can say how far he rowed, looking for the ideal spot rich in codling or saithe, before trying his luck with a simple line, a bone hook and a piece of shellfish gathered for bait.

With the universal patience of the fisherman he waited, the only sounds on the vast face of the ocean were the lap of the water, the occasional cry of a seagull and the steady saw of the line on the gunwale of the boat as the morning wore on and his patience wore thin with it. He had scant return for his morning's work and, perhaps encouraged by the pangs of hunger and thoughts of hungry children, he moved ever further offshore in an effort to find his elusive prey.

Then some instinct drew his eye to the East and to the smudge of white on the horizon. At first only a thin white line, he watched it grow with appalling swiftness, spreading to fill the whole horizon and hurtling towards him. This was no gentle sea fog drifting on a light breeze but a snowstorm of particular size and ferocity, driven by an Easterly gale all the way from the wastes of Siberia. He seized the oars and turned the boat head to wind realising that there was nothing for it now but to ride it out and pray to all the gods that it was only a squall.

An hour later and his words for the gods were more curse than prayer. Not only was he frozen to the marrow but the fierce wind was driving his boat further and further offshore. So it went on, hour after hour into the darkness and eventually into the light once more. He was close to exhaustion, mostly through cold; hunger, thirst and the shear back breaking strain of keeping the boat head to wind; yet despite his best efforts he was many miles out into the empty bleakness of the North Sea. At last too tired to fight any longer he turned the boat and let her run before the wind, curled up in the bottom of his craft and placed his life in the hands of the All Father.

Perhaps the All father heard his prayers and took pity on a brave man at the mercy of the elements, perhaps it was pure good luck, or perhaps it was due in no small part to the skills of the boat builder who had painstakingly constructed his sturdy little clinker built craft. Whatever the reason he awoke to find himself alive and still afloat. The snow had stopped but the wind was still blowing hard. Wearily taking up his oars once more he turned her head to wind and began to row although in his heart he knew it was a hopeless task, the strong winds and the sea pushing him further westwards all the time. For two days he drifted around the North Sea the wind directing him first one way and then the other but rarely towards his home.

On the morning of the third day he awoke to find that the wind had moderated considerably. Scanning the horizon he spotted land to the West. An island perhaps, no mountains certainly, and still quite a long way off. Pulling himself onto his seat he realised that he was in no condition to row. He was exhausted and suffering the effects of 3 days without food and water. If only he had something to eat and drink he might be able to make land. His glance fell on the fishing line still coiled in the bottom of the boat and the thought occurred that perhaps if he could catch a fish, even a little one, it might be enough.

There was a single piece of limpet bait on the hook and he dropped the stone sinker over the side watching intently as it disappeared into the depths. The minutes crept by as he slowly moved the bait up and down in the water. Then he felt a tug on the line, gently at first and then it snapped taut in his hands. Carefully he pulled on the line, the fish felt big and he didn't want to lose it, peering into the water he saw a flash of white as the fish turned its belly to the light.

The fish tugged at the line with less and less power as he raised it towards the surface until finally he was able to ease it over the side of the boat. It was a ling, a big one, and he tore at its flesh with his bare hands, cramming it into his mouth. He paused for a moment as the moist flesh brought relief to dry tissue of his lips and tongue. Chewing slowly on the fish he took a piece and re-baited his hook sending it spiralling once more into the depths. To his surprise the next bite was almost immediate, another big fish and following that yet another. He realised he had found a fruitful fishing ground and prudently took note of his position. He took a careful sighting of the landmarks visible from the spot and how they

were aligned knowing that if he could reproduce that alignment again he would be on or very near the same spot.

Still chewing on the raw fish but feeling much invigorated he picked up his oars and began to row for the shore. The wind was beginning to pick up again but this time it was assisting him and he was confident of making landfall before dark although he still had some considerable way to go. As he rowed the wind increased in ferocity and he was having to battle hard to control the pitching and rolling of his little craft. Soon the land was only visible from the crests of the waves and even then only through a haze of salt spray. Peering over his shoulder he could just make out a headland to starboard and a series of rocky ravines to port. Straight ahead was a small shingle beach and it was for this that he aimed the prow of his vessel. Slowly but surely he approached the shore and just as surely he found himself driven to the left of the beach towards the ravines. He struggled to turn the boat, fighting the oars as the wind and tide steadfastly manoeuvred him towards the razor sharp rocks.

The little boat shuddered on its first contact with the jagged reefs. Driven forward by the wind and waves, it lifted, ploughing ahead, its timbers screaming as they ran over the sharp edges of the rocks. He clung to the seat as the force of the water drove the little craft deep into one of the rocky clefts. Amazingly the boat threaded its way through the narrow passage and buried itself bow first onto the small shingle beach at its head. Each successive wave flung the frail shell of wood further up the little strip till it wedged itself under the low cliff. The force of the impact threw him into the prow of the boat with bone crushing force. The choice was now clear, climb or be drowned like a rat in a barrel. He chose the former and, ignoring the pain from his bruised and battered body, began the arduous climb up the almost sheer face. His fingers numb with cold and his weakened body screaming in protest at every movement, he fought to maintain a hand hold on the slippery rock as the wind buffeted his body but the effort was too much and soon, his last reserves of strength gone, he slid down the cold, wet stone and lay semi-conscious on the beach.

In his dazed condition he became aware of the sound of people shouting and, raising his head, he was dimly aware of a rope snaking down the cliff face. Moments later men began to scramble down and he found himself lifted, tied into a loop in the rope and slowly hauled up the face. As he was gently eased over the top of the cliff and laid upon the grass he dived once more into unconsciousness.

When he awoke he was inside a house similar to his own. A fire burned bright in a hearth in the middle of the floor and for a few moments he almost imagined that he was home. Then reality swept in and he realised that he was a great distance away on the opposite side of the sea and, worse than that, he had no boat with which to return. His ordeal had taken its toll and he was very weak, his body bruised and broken. The people in the house treated him with great kindness and, somewhat to his surprise; he found he was able to understand much of their language.

As the days slipped by it became obvious that his condition was not improving and he realised that he was unlikely to live. Feeling that he owed these people something for trying to save his life he told them of the spot where he had caught the fish. A careful explanation of the landmarks and their alignment would allow the fishermen of this little island to find the spot and reap the benefits of his discovery. Then he made a final request, that he should be given a proper burial and that the remains of his boat should be placed over his body. Shortly after this he died, his strength having sustained him for as long as it could.

The people of the village took his body, prepared it for burial and then dug a shallow pit on the cliffs above the spot where his boat had been wrecked. They laid him in it with his scant worldly goods and then painstakingly hauled the remains of his brave vessel up the cliff face and placed it over the body. A covering of stones and earth completed the mound to discourage the ravens and skuas.

Following the precise directions given to them by the dying stranger the fishermen of the village discovered the spot of which he spoke and fished it for many years. The island upon which he landed eventually came to be known as Fetlar and the fishing ground became known as the Aith Deep and was acknowledged as one of the best fishing spots in the area. Its discoverer passed into legend in stories passed down through the generations and the mound that covered his body on that lonely cliff top became known as the Giant's Grave.

PETTAWATER

Long ago in the days of our ancestors there were many more creatures that wandered the hills of Shetland than we have today. Among the most common were the giants and the trows. The giants were huge men, some standing a full twenty fathoms high, but they were sometimes a little slow and often not particularly clever. The trows however were small and quick and their minds burned with a malevolent intelligence.

At this time a giant lived at the northern end of a range of hills known as the Kames that runs down the spine of the Shetland Mainland. He was the usual giant type, fairly harmless if a little dim, and he lived a pretty blameless life doing a little fishing, keeping his flocks of sheep and growing Shetland oats around what is now the Loch of Voe. He was, however, plagued by a family of trows which lived nearby and as the years went on his problems got worse as more and more of the trows appeared. They stole his sheep and raided his fishing nets. They even became so bold as to disturb his sleep at nights. They climbed over him and shouted into his ears. They pinched and poked and pulled his hair and slid down his giant nose. In truth they became a real nuisance and at last the giant determined that he must be rid of them.

The giant was not a cruel giant and he did not want to hurt the trows so he decided that the best way to dispose of his unwanted neighbours would be to put them all in a kishie[1] and carry them to Norway where they could annoy someone else. With this in mind he set to and wove a kishie of great size that would hold all the trows. The kishie was so big that the bottom was 150 armfuls of straw wide and the top almost twice that. The giant then lay down to sleep with the kishie next to him and when the trows came out he stayed quite still as they clambered all over him and carried out their nightly mischief. The trows were surprised to get no reaction from the giant and thought it mean of him to spoil their fun. Eventually they tired of their sport and gathered in front of him to discuss what might be wrong. This was what the giant had been waiting for and he stretched out his great hands and scooped up the trows, threw them into the kishie and tightened the cord that closed its mouth.

The deed was done and all the trows were now stuck in the kishie complaining and shouting and wriggling around. The giant stood up and tried to lift the kishie upon his back. He heaved and hauled and strained but to no purpose. The kishie full of trows was just too heavy for him to lift. Then an idea struck him. If he could haul the kishie to the top of a nearby hill he would be able to stand below it and ease it onto his back. Once it was there he felt sure he would be able to carry it all the way to Norway and would be rid of the troublesome trows once and for all. So he hauled the kishie up the hill, dragging it along the ground over the rocks and the heather until he finally reached the hilltop. The trows were complaining louder than ever because the journey had been far from comfortable and the giant told them to be quiet as he knelt down and slipped his shoulders under the carrying strap.

The giant rose to his feet with the kishie of trows on his back but, to his horror, he heard a loud ripping noise and the bottom of the kishie where he had been dragging it over the rough ground gave way and all the trows came tumbling out shouting and screaming. They soon realised that they were free and disappeared amongst the heather in the twinkling of an eye, but not before they thumbed their noses at the poor old giant.

In the meantime the giant had overbalanced as the weight came off his back and he fell down on one knee. The spot where his knee landed is still to be seen and is called K'neefell to this day. The area where his other foot landed was badly scored and over time has filled with water and become a loch. It is called Pettawater and if you look carefully you can see the shape of the giants foot and the marks of his toes.

The giant was so disgusted with the whole thing by this time that he decided that it would be simpler to move to Norway himself and he hasn't been seen in Shetland since. The trows however are still there and have given their name to the loch. Older Shetlanders also used to call them pechts and Pettawater is the Lake of the Pechts or trows. It is said that if you know how to spot them they can still be seen on fine summers nights dancing around the loch in the simmer dim[2] to celebrate their victory over the giant.

kishie[1] – straw basket made to be carried over the shoulders

simmer dim[2] – a time of twilight which replaces true nightfall around the summer soltice

THE RAVENS REVENGE

*F*lokki of the Ravens was one of the earliest explorers of Iceland and is the man credited with giving the land its name. The following is a story which claims that he was the main character in a local legend which accounts for the name of a loch and that his famous ravens were in fact Shetland birds.*

In the early part of the ninth century there lived in Norway a man called Flokki. He was an adventurer, a sailor and an explorer, bold and sometimes reckless he lived for the sea and the thrill of new horizons. Only two things held his affection and those were his ship and his daughter Geirhilda. The little girl's mother had died when she was quite young and so she accompanied her father wherever he voyaged. She was her father's pride and joy and he could deny her nothing that it was within his power to give.

Flokki began to hear rumours about a mysterious island in the far North. Some described it as a land of plenty with room for all, green pastures and rivers full of fish. Others called it Hel on earth, a land of fire and ice with vast fields of twisted jagged rocks and huge expanses of glaciers crawling inexorably towards the sea. Whatever the truth Flokki was determined to find out and he prepared his ship for a voyage to this new land. Taking his beloved Geirhilda with him he set sail for the west intending to call along Shetland for fresh water and supplies on his way.

On arrival in Shetland he anchored in Catfirth and went ashore to explore the surrounding countryside. He took a small party of men and went south looking for game, seabirds and seabird eggs and soon was searching along Wadbister Ness while the remaining crew filled their water barrels at the Catfirth Burn. The day went well and although there was little game they found plenty of birds and birds eggs and Flokki was in high spirits when one of his crew shouted that he had found a raven's nest. Flokki scrambled to the cliff top, peered over the edge and sure enough there was the nest with three young ravens in it.

All good Vikings knew that it was not wise to tamper with ravens. They were Odin's birds and served as his eyes and ears in the world of man. They watched the fields of battle with their bright intelligent eyes and told the Valkyries which men were destined for the Halls of the Slain at Valhalla. They were also gifted with speech and their ominous cry of "corp, corp" was said to be a harbinger of death. Most men treated ravens with the greatest of respect but Flokki was not most men. His reckless streak came to the fore and he decided that he would have the young ravens for his own so he clambered down and tucked the three young birds into his collecting bag.

As the men walked back towards the ship a raven appeared. It circled the hunting party skimming low over the landscape, its black wings shining in the evening sunlight. As the group approached the ship it settled on the masthead and croaked a warning of impending doom to the approaching men. Some of the crew began to whisper that this was an ill omen, that it was bad luck and that they should release the raven's children. Flokki would have none of it and cursed them for superstitious fools. As the skies darkened into night the raven circled once more around the camp and flew off into the darkness.

Next day dawned bright and clear and all thoughts of ravens were banished from the mind of the crew as they set off for a last foraging expedition before leaving for Faeroes. This time they set off northwards in high hopes of reaching a local settlement and doing a little trading. Geirhilda was left with the small crew that was to guard the boat and amused herself playing along the shores of Catfirth.

Flokki and his men had another good day, finding a small settlement and bargaining some of their trade goods for fresh meat. As they headed home they were in high spirits that were only slightly dampened by spotting a raven circling some way off.

"Probably a dead sheep" joked Flokki "there's not much else around here."

As they approached the ship they were met by the guard crew who confessed that they had lost Geirhilda. She had been playing quietly on the shore and had wandered off while the crew were busy making last minute preparations for leaving. Flokki was furious and berated them loud and long before organising search parties to look for the little girl. As the men moved off in all directions the raven came skimming over the ship croaking its warning.

Flokki shook his fist at the creature and it flew off inland. It perched on a rock and its cry mocked him. In a fury Flokki pulled out his sword and ran after it but to his surprise it did not fly away but merely fluttered from rock to rock always out of his reach. He pursued the bird some small distance until he reached the top of a low hill and saw spread out before him a lake with a small island in the middle of it. Gazing down he was

horrified to see an object floating in the water near to the shore. Dropping the sword he raced down the hill and waded into the water dreading what he knew he must find.

His scream of anguish brought his men running from all directions to find him standing by the water with the body of Geirhilda in his arms. The little girl had drowned in the dark waters of the loch and the raven had her revenge. The bird sat on a nearby rock its head turned towards the figure of the man with his dead daughter, then the great beak opened and its hoarse cry rang over the moor "Corp, corp, corp."

Flokki buried his daughter alongside the loch which he named Geirhildasvatter in her honour. Then he sailed on towards Iceland stopping off at Faeroes on the way. Catching a favourable southerly breeze he left the Faeroe Islands and after sailing for a day released one of the young ravens. The bird flew in a circle and then turned south back the way they had come. The same happened at the end of the second day when another bird was released but on the evening of the third day the remaining bird circled once and then flew swiftly to the north. Flokki followed it and within a days sailing was in sight of the Icelandic coast. He settled in this new land and was ever after known as Flokki of the Ravens. The loch where Geirhilda met her fate is now known as Girlsta Water.

THE BEACON

*E*ver since King Harald Fine-hair gifted the control of Shetland and Orkney to Earl Rognvald the Powerful the histories of the two island groups have been closely linked. It is appropriate therefore that there are frequent mentions of Shetland in the Orkneyinga, the saga of the Earls of Orkney. Many of the Earls called along Shetland to recruit fighting men for their various expeditions and some of the protagonists fled to Shetland to hide. The most famous example of this latter was by Erlend the Young who took up residence in Mousa Broch after his abduction of Margaret, mother of Earl Harald Maddadarson, whom he subsequently married. Shetlanders also played a notable part in the miracles associated with the canonisation of St Magnus but perhaps the most prominent Shetland connection in the saga was with the coming to power of Earl Rognvald Kali Kolsson.

King Sigurd of Norway granted Kali Kolsson the half of Orkney and bestowed on him the title of Earl. He also gave him the name Rognvald after his ancestor Earl Rognvald Brusason and people thought this to be a good sign. Rognvald Kali Kolsson was to have that part of Orkney that belonged to his uncle the sainted Magnus and the other part was to be held by Earl Paul Hakonsson.

King Sigurd died that winter and Norway was split between his son Magnus and Harald Gilli and Rognvald was one of Harald's loyal supporters. For three years the two kings ruled together but Magnus was unhappy about the settlement and would not acknowledge his father's gift to Rognvald. Finally there was a great battle at Farlev and Harald was forced to flee to Denmark where King Eirik offered him protection. Harald however was far from finished and the following Christmas he attacked Magnus in Bergen and captured and maimed him thus bringing the whole of Norway under his control. He then confirmed the gift of Orkney and the earldom on Rognvald.

Right after this Kol, Rognvald's father, sent envoys to Orkney to offer friendship and to ask Earl Paul to surrender half of the islands as had been decreed. If Paul refused they were to contact Frakokk, wife of Ljot the Renegade of Sutherland, and Olvir Brawl of Rack Wick, her grandson, and offer them an alliance if they would lead an army against Paul. The envoys spoke to Paul but he refused their offers and swore to defend Orkney to the death. The envoys then went south and spoke to Frakokk and she pledged the support of herself and Olvir Brawl to Rognvald's cause. The envoys then returned to Norway and reported how things stood to Rognvald and his father.

Rognvald and his men made ready that winter for the voyage to the islands. Chief among his allies were Solmund Sigurdarson and Jon Petersson, nicknamed Jon Foot. They set off in the summer with only about half a dozen ships and by midsummer were in Shetland. There was no word from Frakokk and soon after their arrival a storm blew up and they were forced to anchor in Yell Sound. The local people gave them a great welcome and they were invited to feast with the farmers of the area. Frakokk had set off from the Hebrides with a dozen small and poorly equipped ships and a few men and they waited for a fair wind to take them to Orkney.

News of Rognvald's arrival in Shetland and the gathering of the Hebrideans reached Earl Paul at Westness on Rousay. He immediately called for Kugi of Westray, Thorkel Flayer and many more of his close advisors to meet with him to discuss the situation. There was however no agreement amongst those present. Some felt that Paul should make peace with one or the other of the opposing forces so he didn't have to fight both. Others felt that he should go south to look for allies of his own amongst his friends and kin in Caithness. Paul chose to ignore all this advice and sent messengers to gather a force of his own to oppose Rognvald. He set off that very day for the mainland with five ships commanded by Eyvnd Melbrigdason, Olaf Hrolfsson, Thorkel Flayer, a man called Sigurd and the Earl himself. With the Earl went his forecastleman Svein Breast-Rope.

Paul arrived at the Mainland at the going down of the sun and followers flocked to his banner all night. Men he had in plenty but no more ships were available. They talked deep into the night and decided to set off for Shetland the very next day. Just after dawn word arrived that sails had been spotted to the south. Earl Paul and his men took to their ships. They were very crowded as they had more than enough men and Paul set some men to work collecting stones to use in the battle. Rowing east of Tankerness they spotted a dozen ships approaching and hastily tied their vessels together to make a fighting platform. The approaching vessels were the Hebrideans under the command of Olvir Brawl ready to give battle. Olvir commanded a larger number of vessels but they were smaller and not so well manned so Earl Paul's man Olaf Hrolfsson attacked the smaller vessels and soon cleared three of them.

Olvir in the meantime had launched a direct attack on Paul's ship and the fighting on its forecastle was fierce indeed. Olvir and Svein Breastrope were leading the opposing forces but when Paul spied Olvir boarding his ship he leaped off the raised deck into the forepeak. Olvir spotted the Earl and grabbing up a spear he threw it at Paul's shield so hard that it knocked him to the deck. Svein, seeing his lord in trouble, heaved a huge stone at Olvir with such force that he was thrown over the side into the water. Although Olvir was dragged on board again by his men he was unconscious and none knew if he was alive or dead. On the fall of their leader some of the men cut the ships loose and started rowing away. Earl Paul chased Olvir and his men all the way to the Pentland Firth and then turned back. Returning to the scene of the battle he took possession of five of Olvir's ships that had been abandoned in the battle and had them refitted.

A large number of men joined him during the night with two more ships and Paul was able to sail for Shetland with twelve fully manned vessels. He arrived in Yell Sound at night and, catching Rognvald's guards completely by surprise, he captured all the ships and money in Rognvald's fleet. In the morning Rognvald gathered his forces and went down to the shore. He invited Earl Paul to come ashore and fight but Paul did not trust Rognvald's Shetland allies and instead invited him to find some ships and meet him at sea. Rognvald knew he stood no chance in a sea battle and that is how things were left as Paul sailed back to Orkney with his, and Rognvald's, fleet and Rognvald was forced to stay the summer in Shetland and beg passage back to Norway on trading ships in the autumn. Rognvald, it was felt, had made rather a fool of himself and this caused some amusement among his enemies and rivals in Norway.

On his return to Norway Rognvald went to see his father and Kol wanted to know if he was happy with the way things had turned out. With a bitter laugh Rognvald said that he could hardly be delighted and that the whole expedition had been a complete disaster. Kol replied that things were never all bad and that he had made friends among the Shetlanders that would serve him well in the future. Rognvald considered this for a moment and then asked his father if he would help him plan his next expedition and accompany him on it for he could see that his father was a cunning thinker and that his advice would be of great assistance to him. His father agreed and advised him right away to contact King Harald and all his other friends in Norway to obtain ships for an expedition in the next spring. This, he said, would give them all winter to gather together the right men for the job and that they would either take Orkney back or die there.

Earl Paul in the meantime had returned to Orkney in triumph and held a great feast of celebration. He appointed friends to raise levees for him in all parts of Orkney and kept a large force of men with him until he received news that Rognvald had left Shetland and returned to Norway. Things were quiet until the Yule feast when Paul invited many friends and allies to his hall in Orphir. An argument arose between Paul's forecastle man Svein Breast-Rope and Svein Asleifarson and Svein Breast-Rope was killed. Paul considered this a great loss although some others thought otherwise. Svein Asleifarson fled to the Hebrides where he stayed over the rest of the winter. Paul was advised to make piece with both Svein and Rognvald but he would have none of it and declared that God would settle the matter between Rognvald and himself.

The Earl ordered that a series of beacon fires be built to warn him of the approach of danger with the first being on Fair Isle. A farmer called Dagfinn Hlodvisson was given responsibility for looking after the Fair Isle beacon and making sure it was lit if an enemy was seen to be approaching from the North or East.

Rognvald spent the winter in Norway meeting friends and relatives and asking for help with a new expedition. In the early spring Kol sent ships abroad to England and Denmark to obtain weapons and provisions and by Easter Rognvald and his father were ready to go to Bergen to see the king. They left with three longships and a cargo ship and picked up a further three fighting ships and the blessing of the king in Bergen. They waited for favourable winds with six longships, three cargo ships and five smaller vessels. A ship arrived from the west with news of Earl Paul's defences and Rognvald called a meeting among his men. He spoke long and eloquently about his cause and finished by saying that this trip would bring him victory or death. Then Kol called upon Rognvald to swear an oath to his dead uncle, the holy Earl Magnus, that should he be granted victory then he would build a cathedral in Kirkwall to house his relics and do him honour. This idea found great favour with Rognvald's supporters and the oath was sworn before them all. Then they put to sea and with a fair wind sailed to Shetland where they were warmly welcomed by the people who had much news from Orkney.

Kol was a cunning man and a great planner. He spoke at length to an old friend called Uni who had helped him on previous occasions and they determined that the beacon on Fair Isle must be sabotaged if Rognvald was to have any chance at landing in Orkney. The two old foxes devised a plan and Kol set off for Fair Isle with a fleet of small boats. When Kol got to an area where he thought they might be visible from Fair Isle he had the sails raised to half mast and then set his oarsmen to row in the opposite direction so that the boats moved very little in the water. By slowly raising the sails up the masts he made it appear to the watchers on the island that the ships were approaching quite fast while the were really not approaching at all. By this clever ploy he hoped to panic the Fair Isle men into firing the beacon when there was no real cause to do so and thus cause discord amongst Paul's men. His strategy worked and the Fair Isle beacon was soon ablaze closely followed by one on North Ronaldsay and so on all the way south to the Orkney mainland. Kol then turned his little fleet around and headed back for Shetland safe in the knowledge that he had sown the seeds of doubt amongst his enemies.

The lighting of the beacon sparked off a full-scale muster of Earl Paul's men on mainland Orkney. Dagfinn Hlodvisson headed south to join the Earl himself and soon all was in readiness to meet Rognvald's forces. For three days they waited with no sign of movement from either Rognvald or his Shetland allies. Then the farmers amongst Paul's men began to complain. They had farms to run, livestock to look after and crops to sow. At first they put the blame on the keeper of the North Ronaldsay beacon Thorstein Rognuson but he would have none of this and placed responsibility squarely on the shoulders of Dagfinn Hlodvisson. The two argued bitterly about the point and eventually Thorstein attacked Dagfinn with an axe and killed him. This was a signal for general mayhem as relatives and friends of both men armed themselves and began to fight. Earl Paul rushed to the scene but even he had difficulty in separating the combatants although eventually order was restored. Kugi of Westray made a speech to the assembled men and explained how he believed that they had been tricked and how such internal strife played right into the hands of Rognvald and his friends. The Earl decided that it might be best in the circumstances for all to return home to allow tempers to cool. A man called Eirik was given responsibility for the Fair Isle beacon.

Meanwhile Uni and Kol had put the second part of their plan into action. Uni took three young Shetlanders in a small boat with a few provisions and some fishing gear and rowed to Fair Isle. Uni explained that he was a Norwegian married in Shetland and had come south with his three sons after a quarrel with Rognvald's men. He spoke scathingly about Rognvald and his Vikings and complained bitterly that the would-be Earl had robbed him. Uni was given lodging on the island and his "sons" went off to the fishing. Uni stayed ashore and looked after the catch. He spent long days on the beach talking to the islanders and making friends. The sly old fox quickly made himself popular locally and he was well trusted. After he had been there some while he went to see Eirik to talk about the beacon. He said to Eirik that he had little to do since his sons were away fishing all day and asked if Eirik needed a man to look after the beacon. Eirik was a busy farmer and was glad to find someone to take this task off his hands and he welcomed Uni's suggestion. Uni was faithful to his word and spent part of his time every day tending the beacon but what Eirik didn't know was that he was taking the opportunity to soak it with water so that it would not burn. When Rognvald made his voyage to Orkney no warning would come from Fair Isle.

When the wind blows from the east and the spring tide runs then it is all but impossible to sail from the island of Westray to the Orkney Mainland. Rognvald and his men knew this and so they waited for these conditions before the set sail from Shetland. When the fleet was sighted from Fair Isle Eirik prepared to sail south to join Earl Paul, but first sent men to Uni to tell him to light the beacon. When the men arrived Uni was nowhere to be found and the beacon was so soaked in water that they could not light it no matter how hard they tried. Eirik realised what had happened and made all speed to tell Earl Paul but Rognvald and his Shetland allies were close behind and reached the northern isles of Orkney before Eirik could reach the Earl.

The strong easterly wind sped Rognvald's ships over the water and soon they arrived at Pierowall on Westray and made their base at the farm of a man called Helgi. The people of Westray gathered together and Helgi and another man called Kugi spoke on their behalf. They asked Earl Rognvald for mercy and when he agreed the people accepted him as their Earl and pledged their allegiance to him.

A curious incident happened to Earl Rognvald shortly after his arrival in Orkney. The following Sunday he attended mass at the church and was standing outside with his friends when they saw sixteen men unarmed and with their heads shaven walking by. They thought this sight to be very strange and discussed who the men might be although they could come to no answer to the question. Rognvald then went through all the nearby villages and farms and the people acknowledged him as their Lord.

Soon after Rognvald heard that some of the men on the island were plotting against him and that a secret meeting was to be held among the conspirators. Some of Rognvald's men took hold of some of the supposed rebels and used them badly even putting one of them, Kugi, in chains. Rognvald had the man released and then went to the meeting himself. Kugi pleaded the cause of the rebels and Rognvald agreed to spare their lives on condition that they took new oaths to support him.

Earl Paul soon heard what was happening on Westray and how many people were joining Rognvald's cause and he called a meeting of his advisors. People said many things and gave many types of council. Some thought Paul should share the Earldom with Rognvald and others felt he should buy Rognvald off by giving him money to go back to Norway. Still others wanted to fight as Paul had already defeated Rognvald in the past.

Earl Rognvald had spies in Paul's camp and soon knew of his opponent's position. He sent messengers to the bishop of Orkney asking him to try to make peace. Negotiations began and a two-week truce was declared. After much discussion the islands were divided, as were the costs of maintaining the Earldom. Rognvald then settled on the Mainland and Paul went to his estate on Rousay.

Shortly after this two of Sven Asleifarson's kin attacked and slew Thorkel Flayer at his farm. They burned him to death with eight of his companions and then went to Rognvald and threatened to join Paul if he would not support them. He agreed to do so and as a result Thorkel's son joined Paul. Rognvald now had such a following in Orkney that he was able to allow many of his Norwegian companions to return home.

Sven Asleifarson now made his way back towards Orkney in a trading ship with thirty men. As they were approaching his home island of Rousay they spotted some men on a headland in the south of the island and Svein told his steersman to make towards them. He then hid twenty of his men, including himself, in their sleeping rolls so that they would not appear to be a large force. Svein's ship rowed up and exchanged greetings with the men on shore. They found out that Earl Paul was on the island and was hunting otters further down the headland with a few of his followers. Svein then put ashore out of sight of the headland and, arming himself and his men, he went in search of Earl Paul. They fell upon Paul's men and slew nineteen of them before capturing Earl Paul and forcing him onto their ship. They then sailed south to Atholl and the court of Earl Maddad and Margaret Hakkonsdottir. Margaret was Paul's sister and he was welcomed there. There was much discussion amongst all the parties concerned.

One day Margaret summoned Svein and told him to sail to Orkney and seek out Earl Rognvald. He was to ask him if he would prefer to share the Earldom with Paul or with Margaret's son Harald who was only an infant at the time. Paul overheard the conversation and came forward. He said that he felt this situation was a result of God's displeasure at himself and his kin and that he was prepared to renounce the Earldom and retire to a monastery. He instructed Svein to tell everyone that he had been blinded and maimed so that none of his friends would try to persuade him to return to Orkney.

Some said that this story was closer to the truth and that Margaret had her brother blinded and then later killed. Whatever really happened Paul never returned to Orkney and was never heard from again. A deal was struck which gave Harald Maddadarson half the Earldom but left control in the hands of Rognvald. Thus Rognvald Kali Kolsson became Earl of Orkney and Shetland.

HERMA AND SAXA

O nce upon a time in the island of Unst there lived two giants who went by the names of Herma and Saxa. Herma lived in a cave called Herman's Haa below the headland of Hermaness and Saxa lived in a similar cavern in the Muckle Pobie of Saxa Vord called Saxe's Haa. There are a good many stories in the islands about these two somewhat less than friendly individuals and their almost continuous bickering.

It was said that Herma once caught a whale of such size that he had nothing to cook it in. He knew that on Saxa's side of the island was a great cavity in the rocks known as Saxa's Kettle and he determined to ask his rival if he could use it for boiling up his catch. Saxa was a shrewd individual however and offered the use of his cooking facilities only if Herma would give him half of the whale. Indignant at this exorbitant demand Herma hurled a huge nearby boulder at the greedy Saxa. As with so many giants his aim was far from good and the rock embedded itself in the sea near to the Horns of Haggmark where it became known as Herman's Stack. Indeed heaving rocks at each other seems to have been a favourite pastime with these two quarrelsome individuals and Saxa's Baa and Herman's Helyak would also appear to have been as a result of their enthusiastic if somewhat misguided attempts to kill each other. Another curious reminder of these creatures was a strange standing stone near to the old Norwick kirkyard that had a hole punched clean through it. It is said that it was used by Saxa to tether his horse and that he made the hole with his thumb. There is unfortunately no record as to the size of the horse involved.

The two giants became even more bitter rivals when they both chanced to fall in love with a beautiful mermaid. The maiden in question made a habit of coming each morning to the Oosta, a low lying islet situated beyond the mouth of Burrafirth and combing her luxurious long blonde hair. The sight of this captivating creature was more than the giants could stand and they both determined to make her their bride. This resulted in further conflict between the two giants and doubtless to more rock throwing but neither of the monsters managed to persuade the

object of his desires to agree to a wedding. Each morning they would both stand at the tip of their respective headlands and declare undying love for the mermaid. The air resounded with their importuning which soon turned to bellows of anger when she once more slipped into the deep without answering their requests. Each blamed the other for his lack of success little thinking that the mermaid found them both equally repulsive and had no intention of marrying either of them.

Eventually the target of the ogres affections got tired of having her morning ablutions disturbed by this pair and determined to make an end of it one way or another. Accordingly she swam close in to the shore and spoke softly to them.

"Dearest ones" she murmured "how can I be expected to decide between two such handsome fellows? I fear we must have some kind of contest to see which of you brave gentlemen will take me for a wife."

The two giants were completely taken in by her soft words and silky tongue and readily concurred that a competition would be quite the thing and that they would abide by the result. The mermaid then explained that she was going to swim to the North Pole and that she wanted the giants to follow her. The winner of the contest would be the giant who either caught her or was closest to her when she reached her destination.

Now neither of the giants could swim although both of them had waded considerable distances offshore to fish and both reckoned that they would be able to walk much faster than the mermaid would be able to swim so they agreed enthusiastically. The mermaid slipped off her rock and swam swiftly northwards while Saxa and Herma splashed into the water and began to take great giant size strides after her. The giants were slower than they thought mainly because they spent too much time pushing and shoving and trying to trip each other up. In fact they were so busy trying to stop each other that they didn't notice the floor of the sea dropping away into deep water until it was too late and they both plunged over the edge. The giants floundered for a few minutes before sinking from sight never to be seen again.Thus the clever mermaid got rid of both her unwelcome suitors and the island of Unst got rid of two of its most troublesome giants.

THE SEA KING

In the far north of the island of Unst there is a long narrow fjord or voe called Burrafirth. The voe faces north; on one side it has the great headland and seabird colony of Hermaness and on the other the brooding presence of the hill of Saxaford. The inlet itself is a pleasant one with a broad sandy beach at its far end and a narrow strip of green separates it from the nearby Loch of Cliff.

It was perhaps a natural place for a seafaring race to settle and legend has it that it provided a home for some of the Norwegian Vikings who fled from the wrath of King Harald Fine-Hair after the battle of Hafrsfjord. The Vikings displaced the native Picts and set up their homes among the barren slopes. Their leader was a man called Thorbjorn Tree-foot who had lost a leg in the battle and now took little active part in the activities of the settlement preferring to advise his son Anlaf from his seat on the high bench. Although his community was not a wealthy one he and his family and followers were at least free which counted for a lot.

The Vikings of Shetland made a habit of raiding across to Norway during the summer months and at the time of our story Thorbjorn's son had taken many of the ablest warriors from their little community and had left for Norway in their only sizeable vessel. It was his intention to spend a few days raiding up and down the coast before returning to Burrafirth with some booty that might be traded to improve the quality of life in their settlement. They had been away for some days now and were expected back at any time. Anxious eyes scanned the mouth of the voe for any sight of the ship and all looked forward to the division of spoils and the little trinkets that might be available for the wives and children of those men taking part.

Among those waiting was Thorbjorn's daughter Auslag who was concerned rather more for the fate of her brother than for any reward that his return might bring. A recent convert to the new Christian religion, she recognised the need for the raids but could not help but feel that there was something dreadfully wrong with all the killing and stealing. It would be good to have her brother back however so she kept a weather eye on the sea as she went about her daily tasks.

At last the ship was sighted rounding the Noup and heading into the voe. It was immediately obvious that something was wrong. The ship should have been forging proudly into the voe and instead it barely limped around the headland. Those who stopped and stared hard noted with some concern that there were perhaps only three or four oars in use on each side instead of the ten that she usually shipped. The ship limped painfully slowly towards the beach and many of the women headed there expecting the worst. Their fears were realised and as the ship approached the shore it was clear that only about ten or twelve of the original crew of thirty were manning the vessel.

Auslag strode down to the shore looking for her brother but although she scanned the men now clambering out of the ship she could see no sign of him. She broke into a run, panic beginning to rise in her breast as she recognised the various men on the shore and realised that Anlaf was not among them. She reached the men just as they began their explanations and listened in horror as their story unfolded.

"The raiding was good and a hold full of prime stuff we had" said Bjorn one of the surviving crew, " we were on the way back and making good time when we spotted a sail on the horizon. A bigger ship it was, proper war galley, and carrying a lot of sail, red and yellow strips and a black snake on it. I'd know that sail again anywhere, may Odin curse him who owns it. Well anyhow we realised that he was after us and there was no way we could outrun him so we reckoned we might as well turn and fight. Like I said she was bigger than us and a bigger crew too probably but we didn't have a lot of choice. Sure enough she grappled us and they swarmed aboard. The leader was a giant of a man, blonde and bearded, with an axe he was using two handed. Cut through us like we wasn't there. Anlaf went to meet him and a sore fight it was. Anlaf moving quick trying to keep away from that axe and the giant swinging at him forehand and backhand both. The lad had courage enough but not the experience and he could only dodge for so long. The blow caught him across the ribs and he died fast at least. By that time there weren't too many of us left and the fight went out of us. They took all we had and left us but their leader came and gave me this. Told me to take it home and tell his family that the boy died well." He held out Anlaf's sword that he had been given by his father who in turn had it from his father before him.

Auslag took the weapon in her hands, the tears starting in her eyes as she thought of the news she would have to impart to her ageing father. The loss of Anlaf was a bitter blow but the loss of so many of the men of the village was worse and threatened the very existence of the settlement itself. The land was barely enough to support them and without the men

to fish and raid the winter would be grim indeed. Grasping the sword she set off for her father's hall while the rest of the people made ready to bury their dead.

Two days later a young boy scrambling along the cliffs just south of Hermaness spotted a longship bearing down upon the Tonga Stack in a freshening breeze. The ship had the red and yellow sail with the black serpent on it that had been so recognisable at the recent attack on their own ship. The boy lay down and watched as the ship approached. He realised that she was sweeping in too close and was not aware of the sharp reefs that lay on the seaward side of the stack. He watched as she struck, going at speed before the breeze she ripped her bow apart on the razor like rocks and began to fill with water immediately. A few of the crew including the blonde giant leapt from her side and began to swim for the shore. The water was cold and the surf running high and the boy watched as one after the other of the pirates slid under the waves to appear no more. All except for their leader who made it to the base of the steep cliffs and began to drag himself up the sheer face. It was clear that even a man of his huge strength had been severely weakened by the struggle in the freezing water and the boy watched as he hauled himself into a cave half way up the cliff and did not reappear.

After watching for a few minutes the boy ran back to the village to tell everyone what he had seen. Almost the entire population accompanied him back to the cliff top where their enemy, they hoped, was now trapped. Standing on the cliff edge Thorbjorn shouted over the edge. "Dog of Hel stay in your kennel unless your prepared to die today. You took my son from me and fathers and brothers from half our village. Don't think your death will be easy sea wolf." There was no reply from the cave and Thorbjorn set guards at the cliff top and went back to talk things over with the few men who were left amongst them. To go down the cliff face after the man would be suicide so they considered that it would be better to leave the man there until he either starved and decided to climb up and fight them. Thorbjorn spent the evening dreaming up ever more spectacular ways in which to put his hated enemy to death.

Auslag had different thought on her mind as she went to bed that night. She could not help but think if the man in the cave and the way he must be feeling. Cold, hungry and trapped like a rat in a trap, she found it difficult to imagine what his thoughts might be. She felt in her heart that the man was no worse or better than the men from their own community had been. After all they had left Burrafirth to raid, to steal, rape and murder. Why should this man die a horrible death for doing what his people had done for many years? Next day she could not get the trapped man out of her mind and she slowly determined that if she could do anything about it he should not die.

All day a relay of men, women and children visited the cliff top, some to hurl insults, some merely out of curiosity. There was little or no response from the cave below and some people began to wonder if the man might not already have succumbed to cold and exhaustion. Auslag decided she must act that night if she was to act at all and made her preparation accordingly. During the day she collected a rope, an iron spike, a hammer some food and water and a small knife and put them in a sack which she hid in an outhouse. She also prepared a sleeping draught in a flagon of ale which she hoped would dispose of the guards.

Around midnight she took the flagon and the sack and made her way to the cliffs. The guards were glad of the ale and she wandered off and hid at a spot where she could watch them without being seen. In very short order they fell asleep just as she had planned and she made her way back to the cliff. Driving the iron spike into the ground she quickly tied the rope to it and threw it over the edge. Then she threw herself flat and called to the man in the cave.

"For the love of God if you would live then climb now or die where you sit."

A voice replied from the darkness "I care not for your God but if I am to die then better I should die in the open air than in this den." Then the rope went taught and Auslag was able to see a dim shape moving in the darkness as the reever began his ascent. He heaved himself up to the cliff top and stood looking around him, surprised to see only Auslag and the sleeping guards. Auslag looked him up and down wanting to see what kind of man she had rescued. He was very tall and broad with a face that was strong rather than handsome. The clothes he wore were of fine quality and he had a large gold arm ring on his left arm. His look was proud but at the same time it did not smack of arrogance just confidence in his own ability.

"What is your name and what game are you playing lady?" he murmured looking at the young girl in front of him from under his heavy eyebrows. "Why do you help your enemy and your peoples enemy?"

"My name is Auslag Thorbjornsdottir and our Christian God says that we should love our enemies as our friends. You are an evil man, a killer and a thief, but I cannot stand by and see you killed. Take these and go south, there you will find a settlement called Westing and you can steal a boat and leave this island forever. All I ask is that you swear to me that you will not return." she said handing him the bag with the food, water and the knife.

"That's easy done," he replied " if I ever see this pox ridden lump of rock again it will be too soon. I thank you lady though I doubt if any of your fellow villagers will agree with your actions. You can rest assured that you will never see me again. This I, Gutrom of Denmark, do swear by the ring of my fathers." With that he set off to the south keeping below the skyline and moving easily in the dark. After a few yards he turned and called back to her "There is a debt between us lady and I will repay it if it takes me all my days, this I also swear." Auslag went back to her bed and prayed to her God that she had done the right thing.

The escape caused no little excitement the next day and of course the guards were roundly berated for falling asleep on duty. Too much ale was the general agreement and the men were more than a little shame faced for some weeks afterwards. No word was heard about the escapee although the disappearance of a small boat from Westing seemed to indicate that he had made good his escape. Thorbjorn was of course furious but the business of trying to survive the winter soon occupied people's minds and the man was forgotten.

It was late May in the following year that a ship was spotted rowing into the mouth of Burrafirth. A longship of perhaps thirty oars a side it was far too big to be a local ship and must be from Norway or some such place. People crowded to the shore half fearful and half hopeful. The winter had been hard with the people close to starvation and the chance to trade fish or skins would be welcome but this did not have the look of a trader. A raid would gain the raiders little as there was not much worth stealing but there was always the risk that they might be looking for slaves. The few surviving men looked to their weapons and prepared to die in defence of their people.

The strange ship beached itself and some twenty or thirty warriors spilled over its side and strode up the beach. A tall man lead them up towards the waiting villagers and stopped in front of Thorbjorn who stood a little in front of his people with his hand on his sword hilt.

"I am seeking Auslag Thorbjornsdottir," he said "Is this where she lives?"

"It is" answered Thorbjorn "and what do you want with my daughter?" Auslag moved forward to stand beside her father and the man acknowledged her with a slight inclination of his head.

"She has earned the favour of King Gutrom the Dane. The King is returning to Denmark after a successful campaign against the Angles in Britain and has a mind to reward the lady for a service." He gestured towards the ship and a number of men scrambled over the side carrying two large chests which they brought forward. The chests were opened to reveal huge quantities of silver coin mostly of southern origin. "The reward is hers as a debt paid but hear this well, if any harm should come to Auslag Thorbjornsdottir because of her help to the sea king then he will fall upon this village with fire and sword and no man, woman or child shall remain alive."

With that he turned and marched down the beach and back onto his ship. Thorbjorn stood for some time looking at the wealth before him and then turned to his daughter.

"I do not know what part you played in this nor do I wish to. Reward is better than revenge when our people are starving and if you are willing to share your riches there can be little doubt that your Christian ways have saved our little settlement."

"Father you know that what is mine belongs to all. With this money we can build a stronger community and will not need to raid to survive the winters. Now at last we can live in peace instead of depending on the death of others for our life."

The community of Burrafirth became a prosperous one because of Gutrom's silver and Auslag became a respected leader of her people upon the death of her father. The cave in which the sea king was trapped and from which he was rescued became known as Gutrom's Hole.

THE HOODED MAN

An old farmer at Sumburgh Head in the south of Shetland was waiting patiently by his little open fishing boat for a companion to turn up to fish with him. All the other boats in the district had already gone out and the farmer was becoming increasingly impatient. A stranger in a white cowl came walking along the beach and approached the farmer asking him why he wasn't fishing with the rest of the men. The farmer replied that he was waiting for his companion but that if he didn't turn up shortly they would miss the tide. The stranger offered to take the man's place for a share of the fish and the farmer agreed but said that he would have to take the boat's share as he was a poor man and had a family to feed. This was agreed and they hauled the boat down the beach and set off, the stranger rowing strongly.

They rowed out well past Sumburgh Head and round Horse Island. The current there was very strong and the area was full of rip tides and whirlpools. The custom was to fish along the edge of the tides but to be careful not to be drawn into them for fear of the boat being torn apart by the strength of the currents. The farmer warned the stranger of this danger several times but the hooded man seemed to have no regard for his own safety and paid little heed to the warnings. So disturbed was the farmer that he could hardly concentrate on his fishing.

Eventually the inevitable happened and the little craft was drawn into the centre one of the tidal streams. The water swirled dangerously around the prow of the boat as the stranger pulled hard on the oars. The craft bobbed and weaved in the swell as he guided it though the whirlpools and eddies. The farmer was so frightened by this time that he had stopped fishing altogether and was weeping to himself. He cried out to the stranger " A curse on you and on my ill luck, I'm going to die here today and then what's to become of my family. They will starve for sure"

The stranger laughed and said " Dry your eyes old man and see to the fishing lines. He who led us in here will surely lead us out again. In the meantime we might at least catch some fish."

The farmer began to pull in the lines and to his astonishment there was fish after fish on the hooks and all big ones. They fished for an hour

and the boat was full when the stranger at last pulled it out of the tide and headed for shore. The farmer was mightily relieved to be safe once more and astonished at the quantity of fish they had caught in such a short time.

When they reached shore the stranger told the farmer to divide the catch as he wished and give him his third share. Many of the poor people of the district had gathered at the beach in the hopes of picking up a few small fish if the catch was good but to everyone's amazement the stranger divided all of his share amongst those that were waiting and would keep none for himself.

As the stranger left he walked up a steep grassy bank and slipped where the grass was wet from the rain, tumbling all the way to the bottom. A woman seated nearby laughed and this caused some merriment among the rest of the people who also smiled or laughed at the stranger's predicament. Rising to his feet he spoke this verse.

> *Wittily the woman*
> *Mocks my wear,*
> *But she laughs overlong*
> *And may not laugh last.*
> *Early I sailed out,*
> *Eagerly, and fully*
> *Furnished for fishing.*
> *Who'd figure me for an Earl?*

Earl Rognvald Kali Kolsson smiled to himself as he walked away for who indeed could know an Earl when he was dressed as a fisherman.

THE BEAR

During the thirteenth and fourteenth centuries there were times when Shetland was removed from the control of the Earldom of Orkney and Shetland and was under the direct rule of the King of Norway. As with most kings he was of the opinion that his subjects should pay him taxes and to this end he sent his representative, his befalingsmann, over each summer to collect his dues. The king's officer would travel around the islands with a small escort of soldiers, set up camp at various places and wait for the people to bring what was owed. He would also listen to any petitions to the king or complaints and generally the whole process went on for at least one and maybe several days. The local udallers (freemen) seized the chance to do a bit of trading with anything that was left over when the king had taken his share and merchants followed the befalingsmann around in the hope of selling their wares. In fact the whole occasion was turned into a minor holiday and even paying taxes became a little less painful as a result.

Nobody in those days had much in the way of spare cash and for the most part the befalingsmann had to accept payment in whatever people had to spare. It might be smoked mutton or dried fish or perhaps oats or butter. The locals would weigh out their produce on a wooden balance beam called a bismar and would then have it checked by the befalingsmann on a bismar certified by the king himself. If the two weights didn't match there was often some spirited discussion about the accuracy or otherwise of the various scales and about the honesty of the various parties involved. After this entertainment there was usually some negotiation as to the exact amount to be handed over and everyone went away happy.

Our story starts on just such a day on the island of Fetlar and concerns the fate of a local udaller called Jan Teit. Jan was a powerful man. Strong and handsome it was said that he had many contacts in Norway and was even known to the king himself. Unfortunately however Jan was a hot-tempered individual and his lack of control sometimes lead him into trouble. Despite this he was well thought of in Fetlar and a man of some note.

This particular year Jan had decided to pay his taxes in butter and had brought what he considered to be sufficient packed in a small barrel. He gave it to the befalingsmann to be checked and was less than happy to be told that he was well short of the weight needed. A heated argument ensued with Jan calling down the curse of the Gods on all crooked tax collectors and the befalingsmann threatening dire consequences if the balance of the payment was not met. The scene soon drew a small crowd and many of Jan's neighbours supported his argument accusing the tax collector of dishonest dealing and personal greed. The befalingsmann held up the king's bismar and pointed out that the king himself had certified the scale. At this Jan lost his temper and grasping his own bismar he struck the king's man a powerful blow on the head. The befalingsmann fell dead at his feet and the crowd gathered around Jan chasing the soldiers of the escort back to their ship where they immediately set sail back to Norway. The udallers then repossessed their already paid taxes and congratulated Jan on his fight against the corrupt befalingsmann.

Jan was no fool and once he had calmed down he realised that he was now in a great deal of trouble. To kill a king's man was a certain death sentence and even if he went on the run the king would hunt him down and administer his justice in a very permanent way. Jan discussed the matter with his friends and concluded that his only option was to journey to Norway and throw himself on the king's mercy. Perhaps the best that he could hope for would be a quick death but that was better than being hunted like a dog. Jan took ship for Norway where his fate awaited him.

Jan appeared before the king as a supplicant. He wore the white robe that symbolised his contrition and went with his head and feet bare to demonstrate his humility. He had however managed to conceal a small axe under his robe on the off chance that the befalingsmann might have friends at court who were not inclined to wait for the king's justice. He walked into the throne room of the Norwegian king and stood with his head bowed waiting for the king to speak. There was a moments silence and then the king burst out laughing. Jan looked up in surprise and found that the king was staring at his feet.

"Mother of God Jan those are the ugliest feet I've ever seen in my life," roared the king. "How can a man appear before his sovereign lord with such ugly things on display."

Jan looked down at his feet which he had to acknowledge were far from pretty. They were covered on corns and bunions and hard horny bits of skin. They were indeed as ugly as the king had said.

"If they offend you my Lord then I shall cut them off." cried Jan taking out his axe and starting to hack at his feet. The king called to his guards to stop him and take the axe away. Then he looked at Jan standing there with the blood streaming from his feet yet still proud and undaunted. This was a man he could use he thought, perhaps to solve a rather difficult little problem he had. And if he got killed in the process then justice would have been served just as well.

"Well Jan" said the king "I'll tell you what I will do. Any man with so little caring for his own skin should be brave enough to risk all to win his freedom. I'm having a bit of a problem with a bear in the nearby forest that seems to have developed a taste for human flesh. It's become so dangerous that hardly a traveller can pass through the wood. So I will make a wager with you. Bring me the bear alive and I will spare your life but if you can't capture it alive then pray that it gives you a swifter death than I would. What's it to be Jan, the bear or the blood eagle?"

Jan opted for the bear because he figured that even a slim chance was better than no chance at all. The chance was very slim however and now here he was about to face this fierce creature with no weapons and not even any proper clothes. All he had was a set of chains and a muzzle that the king had thoughtfully provided. He needed time to think and on the way to the forest he passed the home of an old wise woman of his acquaintance so he decided to stop and ask her advice.

The wise woman invited Jan in and sat him down at the table. She gave him a bowl of soup and listened carefully while he explained his predicament. After a few moments thought she said " It was butter got you into this mess and its butter will get you out of it. Go to the forest and pick a spot where you can hide and the bear won't find you. Then come back here and I will give you a barrel of butter with a special herb mixed into it that will put the animal to sleep. Perhaps we will surprise the king yet."

Jan did as he was told and found a spot where he could hide from the creature yet still keep the barrel of butter in view. Then he returned to the cottage and picked up the barrel from the old woman. She warned him to be careful and sent him on his way with her blessings.

Jan set the barrel on a stump in the middle of a clearing and hid himself in the branches of a nearby tree to wait for the bear to appear. After about forty-five minutes he heard noises in the undergrowth nearby and the bear appeared at the far edge of the clearing. Jan was astonished at the size of the creature which must have stood over 10ft tall on its hind legs. He began to have doubts as to whether any herb could quieten such a formidable beast. The bear stood on the edge of the clearing for a few moments sniffing the air. Its beady little eyes roved over the ground and it swung its head from side to side scanning the trees. Jan was well hidden however and the bear soon moved towards the tree stump and began to feast on the butter. Soon it was all finished and to Jan's delight the bear promptly curled up and went to sleep.

Jan was mindful of the warnings to be careful and threw several branches at the bear to ensure that it would not awaken while he was chaining it. The old woman was as good as her word though and the bear was not going to wake in a hurry so Jan seized his chance and fastened the chains and muzzle onto the gigantic creature. He wondered what would happen when the bear awoke and found itself chained and he prayed that the fetters would be strong enough to hold it. To his surprise the animal was quite docile and Jan began to suspect that there might be more to the butter than just a sleeping draft. Whatever the cause of its demeanour the bear allowed Jan to lead it in chains back to the town and even into the king's throne room.

They would have made a comical pair entering the throne room, Jan hobbling on his injured feet and the bear swaying on its hind legs, but when people saw the size of the creature then all smiles died on their lips. There was a hushed silence as the odd pair made their way to the throne. "Well Jan" said the king " I confess that I never expected to see you alive again but you've achieved what many of us thought to be impossible. You've kept your side of the bargain and now I must keep mine. You're life is spared and you are free to return home. Only one condition I will place on you and that is that you must take the bear with you and keep it safe and well for the rest of its natural life. Maybe it will remind you to be more careful of your temper in future."

So Jan and his bear arrived back in Fetlar and people listened in near disbelief as he told his extraordinary story. They couldn't deny that the bear was real enough so most accepted that the story was probably a true one. Jan was considered to be the luckiest of men to survive the encounter and he soon settled back down on his farm with the bear. Problems soon arose with such a large animal on such a small island and the bear began to make a real nuisance of itself. It kept breaking its bonds and wandering around the island so that no domestic animal too slow to outrun it was safe. Apart from that it had a disturbing tendency to demolish buildings in its search for food and people got tired of rebuilding sheds and re-thatching byres.

Eventually all the udallers in Fetlar got together and approached Jan saying that he would have to do something about his charge. Jan replied that he couldn't see what to do as the bear was under the protection of the king and couldn't be killed but he would try to find a solution. He thought long and hard and eventually decided that the only way out of his predicament was to maroon the bear on one of the small islands between Yell, Unst and Fetlar. The island he chose was Lingey and the bear was soon chained to a very stout post on the southern end of the island. Jan had to make the journey to the island every day summer and winter to feed the beast and make sure that it had not broken loose. The poor creature wandered at the end of its chain there for the rest of its natural life and wore a circular track into the ground that was called the Bear's Bait. Jan was a changed man after this experience and kept a much tighter reign on his temper, particularly when dealing with the king's taxmen.

YELA BRUN

The little people of hill and stone, called by Shetlanders the trows or pechts, have long been a feature of rural life in Shetland. Over the years their contact with the world of man has decreased and in the last few centuries they have limited their activities to the kidnap of an occasional fiddler and a variety of more or less malignant tricks played on unsuspecting crofters. The trows dealt with by our Norse ancestors were of a different breed, bolder and more dangerous. The Vikings reckoned the trows to be the remnants of a degenerative race which had existed in the islands before the coming of the Scandinavians. A small and dark race that lived below the ground and only appeared at twilight to work its mischief. The trows were thieves and kidnappers and no one was safe to venture out on the long dark winter night when they held sway over the land. Even the bravest would travel only by moonlight and then only in company.

The little community of Uyeasound in the Island of Unst was particularly beset by these creatures and the people were at their wits end. Crops were spoiled in the fields, lambs went missing, and peats hard won as fuel vanished into the night. Nothing was safe and it was even rumoured that dead infants in the village were changelings substituted by the trows. On and on it went for season after season and the residents of this once fertile and prosperous village sank into a black depression. Fights and quarrels became more and more frequent as the strain of living under the curse of the trows took its toll.

One day in the late autumn the village received an unusual visitor. A priest of the new Christian religion stopped to speak to the Jarl and offer his services as a healer. A man from far distant Ireland who followed the white Christ, he had travelled far to bring the worshippers of Odin to the new faith but was wise enough in his trade to know that the first step was to make himself useful before trying to convert the heathens. He therefore began moving from farm to farm with his bag of herbs and potions offering cures for the afflicted. He was greatly skilled and many recovered under his ministrations that otherwise might have died. As the winter progressed he began to receive invitations from farmers to come

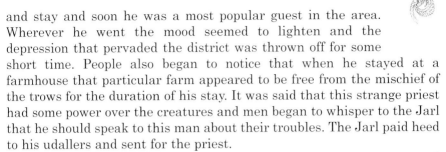

and stay and soon he was a most popular guest in the area. Wherever he went the mood seemed to lighten and the depression that pervaded the district was thrown off for some short time. People also began to notice that when he stayed at a farmhouse that particular farm appeared to be free from the mischief of the trows for the duration of his stay. It was said that this strange priest had some power over the creatures and men began to whisper to the Jarl that he should speak to this man about their troubles. The Jarl paid heed to his udallers and sent for the priest.

The priest listened carefully as the Jarl described the trials and tribulations which the village suffered at the hands of the trows and asked if the priest could suggest any solution. The priest confessed that he had already been aware of some of what was going on as many of his patients had blamed their ills on the creatures. He asked the Jarl for time to consider and pray to his God before giving an answer and the Jarl agreed to wait till the next morning for a reply. The holy man stayed up most of the night praying and thinking about both the trows and his mission. He felt sure that if he could vanquish the trows then he would be able to convert the whole area to Christianity at one go and that perhaps that was why God had directed his footsteps here in the first place. By morning he had decided on a course of action and went to the Jarl.

"I am convinced that it is the power of my God which is driving away the trows" he said, "if you build me a church where I can worship my God then I believe that his power will be strong enough to drive these evil spirits from your land and bring prosperity back to your people."

The Jarl summoned a council of the elders of the village and they considered the request made by the priest. Some felt that they would incur the wrath of the old gods in building this church and others felt that the old gods had done little for them up till now so they were willing to take the risk. After much debate it was decided that the church would be built and that all the farmers would contribute, as they were able, to its construction.

The building itself was to be of stone but the roof was to be wood and the farmers began hauling the necessary supply from the piles of driftwood hauled above the shoreline. They set to work on the construction that very day digging out the site and hauling rock from the nearby hillside to form the foundations. They left at sunset well pleased with their day's efforts and looking forward to starting on the walls the next day.

Slowly but surely the work progressed with the huge boulders from

nearby being carefully manoeuvred into place within the thick walls. The men worked hard and were proud of what they had been able to achieve. Each day the priest visited the site and watched the men as they laboured and he was content that soon he would have a place where he and perhaps some others might be able to worship.

When the walls had reached head height there came a violent storm that raged overnight. Thunder and lightning rent the skies and the winds blew with great ferocity so that people were afraid that the roofs would blow off their houses. In the morning the men scheduled to work on the church trudged up to the site and were met by a scene of complete devastation. The great walls had been torn down to their very foundations and the building stone had been scattered far and wide over the landscape. The men stood in awe of the forces that must have been unleashed to achieve such destruction and some began to mutter darkly about Thor and his displeasure. Others however took time to examine the ground and found the marks of many small feet and knew that the trows had taken action to stop their work.

The Jarl and the priest soon arrived and discussions took place at length as to what should be done. At last it was agreed that a watch must be kept on the site every night and the priest agreed that he would sleep there if one of the local men would stand guard and watch over him. This was put into practice that very night and the priest slept soundly with the Jarl himself watching over him. So it went on for many nights. The men took turns to guard the sleeping priest and his very presence seemed to be enough to keep the trows away.

At last the walls were finished and it was time to put the roof on but a storm blew up and the wind and rain delayed construction for several days. The priest and his guard stayed in the shell of the building during these stormy nights and had an uncomfortable time of it. On the final night of the storm the man set to guard the priest was young and headstrong and although strong warnings were laid on him not to leave the presence of the holy man he decided that he would go out and have a look around rather than sit still with the rain running down the back of his neck. The priest awoke to find him gone and shouted his name aloud hoping to get a reply from the darkness outside the walls. No answer came and the priest decided that he should go and look for the young man. He did not have to search far as just outside the door he found his body with the head smashed into a bloody mess.

As he knelt over the body he felt strong hands gripping him from behind and a sack of some kind was forced over his head. He then had the impression of being lifted into the air and carried with great speed by a great many small but very swift individuals. Suddenly the air about him was still and the noise of the storm abated. He was carried for a little while longer and then was thrown roughly down onto the ground. The sack was pulled from over his head and he found himself in a cavern of some kind carved out of the solid rock lit only by two smoky torches. A crowd of small creatures human in shape but dark and malevolent in appearance surrounded him. They crowded every corner of the cavern and stared at him from the shadows with bright eyes. Then one of them stepped forward and spoke to him, its voice course and its speech stilted and uneven.

"Holy man, it is not yet the time of your God. We are not ready to depart this place. Some day you will have the power to drive us out but the darkness still holds for now. It is you who must leave and serve your God in another place. Sleep now holy man and join your God." With that the creature stepped forward and laid its hand on the priest's brow. A flash of light seared across his vision and then he descended into blackness and knew no more.

The following morning the storm had abated and the men of the village turned up to begin work on the roof of the church. They were horrified to discover the body of the priest's companion and even more horrified to find the priest missing. An extensive search found the priests body some distance to the north on a low hill overlooking the Loch of Watlee. No mark could be found on his body and he lay as if asleep. When the body was raised to be carried back for burial a spring burst forth from the ground on which it had been laying, the water gently bubbling its way down the slope towards the loch.

The church at Uyeasound was never finished and the remains of the site, called Glatnakirk, can still be seen to this day. The waters of the spring proved to have great healing properties and it became known as Yella Brun, the spring of healing. It was said that its waters could also discourage trows if sprinkled on the doorstep of a house. It too can still be seen today and local custom dictates that anyone drinking from the well should leave three stones on the cairn by its side.

The trows continued to manifest themselves in the district for many years afterwards but never again were they as fierce or as reckless. As the Christian religion grew in the islands they dwindled into legend and it is said that the last trows left Shetland to go to the Faeroe Islands in the 1800s as a result of a minister whose sermons were so powerful that the trows were quite unable to live with the noise of them.

GEITISHAMRAR

T hidrandi the Old had two sons and they lived at a farm in Njardvik near Fljotsdal in Iceland. The oldest son was called Thrum-Ketil and the other was named Thorvald. Thidrandi was a much respected man and chieftain amongst his people. He died aged one hundred and thirty six when a ram broke his thighbone and the wound festered.

Thorvald, the younger son, was a likely youth strong and handsome but of a quiet and peaceable nature. Ketil was extremely strong but ugly and with a violent temper resulting from a strange illness. He was of a naturally taciturn nature but every two weeks or so he would get violent shaking fits and when these were upon him a great anger would manifest itself and he would attack anything or anyone who came into his vicinity.

When their father died the brothers quarrelled over their inheritance. Ketil believed that as the oldest he should have the right to make all the decisions regarding the farm and that Thorvald should obey him in all things. Despite his good nature Thorvald was not prepared to accept this and so it was decided that the property should be divided and each brother should go his own way. Ketil however refused to share his inherited authority as chieftain and this led to bad blood between the brothers. So Thorvald rented out his lands and cattle and took all his possessions and left Njardvik.

Thorvald journeyed through the mountains of Fljotsdal to a place called Unaos where he found a ship making ready to sail. Thorvald bought himself trade goods and booked passage on the ship meaning to go abroad and make his fortune. Luck did not attend him however and when they cleared the coast the ship could not pick up a favourable wind. They spent a great part of the summer sailing around the coast waiting for a fair breeze only to be caught in a violent offshore storm. The storm drove them southeastward and in the darkness with violent wind and breaking seas they were shipwrecked upon the treacherous reefs of Shetland. Despite the loss of the ship the passengers got ashore safely but all their goods were lost.

Thorvald waited for some time to see if any of his goods would drift

ashore but after three days all he had found was a large spear so he left and made his way to the home of the Earl of Hjatland. This ruler's name was Bjorgolf and he was then a man of great age. Although a good ruler and popular with his people the Earl had a reputation as a troubled soul and smiled and laughed but seldom. Thorvald arrived at the time of the evening meal and sat quietly by the door. The following morning he presented himself to the Earl and greeted him warmly. The Earl responded well to his greeting and asked him who he was and where he had come from.

Thorvald answered that he was an Icelander newly shipwrecked on the shores of Shetland and had lost everything. He presented himself as penniless and begged the Earl to allow him to stay the winter, as he was keen to be one of the Earl's men. The Earl replied that given his circumstances he perhaps didn't have much choice but if he wanted he could have a seat on the lower benches. Thorvald took his seat among the slaves and freeborn servants of the Earl and was well pleased. Among them he was cheerful and peaceable and he learned many things about the Earl's household. Thus winter passed and Yule drew near.

As the season of merriment drew near the household sank into a deep gloom. The Earl himself was particularly downhearted and even the presence of his pretty young wife and two fine sons could not raise his spirits. Thorvald was curious and asked his bench mates what was the cause of all this misery but no one wished to tell of it and his new friends turned away and spoke of other things.

As Yule approached Thorvald began to be troubled by strange dreams. The men lying next to him were disturbed by his tossing and turning and wanted to wake him but the Earl said no and that he should be left to enjoy his dream. When he awoke the men asked him about his dream but he would not tell of it. A scant two days before the Yule festival Thorvald went to the Earl and asked to speak to him in private.

Thorvald then asked the Earl if he would tell him what it was that made the people so unhappy in a season that should bring happiness. The Earl rebuffed him saying that it was none of his business and that if he wanted the Earl's favour he should ask fewer questions. Thorvald apologised for his question and asked the Earl if he would read his dream for him and the Earl bade him go ahead although he had little skill in such matters. Thorvald then described his dream.

"I was alone, walking towards the sea, dressed as you see me now but with my spear in my hand. It was a clear day and I could see the path before me. When I came to the sea the tide was going out and there was a broad strip of sand exposed. Where the sand finished there was a ridge of rock with a cleft in it full of seaweed. When I climbed through this cleft and looked up onto the land once more there was a great hill before me and a steep rock slope leading down to cliffs right above the sea. Climbing back down on the other side of the ridge I waded in shoal water round a spur of the cliff and came to a shingle beach which I followed for a long time. Ahead of me was a large cave and a light was shining so that there were no shadows. Within the cave was a great pillar of iron and bound to this pillar was a woman. Fastened with chains of iron she was with a great lock on one end. I dreamt that I managed to free this woman and we fled back along the beach and past the shoals but then it seemed that some creature pursued us and I was greatly in fear of it. I think that we met in my dream this creature and I but I have no recollection of what passed between us. It was then that I must have disturbed my fellow sleepers for I awoke soon after."

The Earl had reddened with fury as he listened to Thorvald and when he finished he burst forth. "Strange it is for you to say you are dreaming of things which other people have told you. My grief is deep enough already without you reminding me of my daughter's disappearance. He who told you of this against my command should be punished."

Then Thorvald denied that any had told him this tale and said that he had truly dreamed it, and the Earl was silent for a time and then he replied: " Two futures there may be for you, either you are gifted with foresight or you will very shortly be dead." Thorvald asked the Earl to tell him of the tragedy that so blighted his life and the Earl told his tale.

"A daughter I had before these fine sons of mine. A beautiful girl, accomplished in all things and a great joy to me. At the festival of Yule last year she vanished from my hall, spirited away by a giant. Geiter his name is and he lives in the place you have described which is called Geiteshamar. The hill is called Geitissulur. He is a wicked creature and has caused great harm to my people injuring both men and cattle on his raids. No injury he has done however is as great as the kidnap of my daughter and I would gladly give her to any man who was bold enough to rescue her."

Thorvald felt it unlikely that she would ever be rescued and said so. The Earl made promises that the girl would not be empty handed and pressed Thorvald into taking some action. The Earl reminded Thorvald of his dream and the obligation that placed upon him. Thorvald was reluctant to accept that he was obliged to do anything and went to his seat. He was quiet for the rest of the day taking no part in the sport of his fellows.

Later that night when all men were asleep Thorvald picked up his spear and quietly left the Earl's hall. Going down to the sea he turned and headed north along the sand. Everything happened as in his dream. There was the broad strip of sand, the cleft and the seaweed, ahead of him the hill and the rock face. He climbed down and waded through the shoal then walked swiftly along the shingle until at last the cave which he had been expecting came into sight. He slowed creeping quietly towards the cave and looked inside.

Against one wall was a huge bed, much bigger than any which he had ever seen. Thorvald thought that if two men such as he were to lie end to end the bed would still be long enough with room to spare and it was almost as wide as it was long. The bed hangings were of rich tapestry and the covers of the most luxurious materials. The mattress was as thick as a man's waist and filled with the finest down. Strangest of all above the bed there hung a large sword in a beautifully worked scabbard. Thorvald went over to the bed and grabbed the sword from its place. It came down and brought a large number of stones with it and he had to spring out of the way. The sword had iron hilts with no ornament and when Thorvald drew it from its scabbard the blade was a dark green with brown edges. There was no spot of rust on the blade and Thorvald felt this was the most beautiful sword he had ever seen and immediately wanted it for his own.

On the far side of the cave he spotted heaps of goods. He could see all kinds of Icelandic merchandise there as well as many other luxuries and the best of food and drink. In the centre of the cave was the iron pillar and, just as he had seen in his dream, bound to it was a young woman in a red tunic. Though the Earl had said much of the fine qualities of his daughter Thorvald was amazed at the beauty of the woman before him. He went across and greeted her and she replied that she was called Droplaug and was the daughter of Earl Bjorgolf. She then begged him not to tarry in that place as the monster Geiter was more terrible than he could possibly imagine and that besides he could not hope to free her from the chains that bound her to the pillar.

Thorvald swore he would not leave the cave unless she was with him and once again she begged him to leave. "The giant treats me well although he chains me to this pillar each night while he goes hunting. He handles me gently and I want for nothing except my freedom."

"And yet your freedom you shall have." said Thorvald and drawing the sword he struck the chain such a blow that it parted and fell away from the pillar. Then they fled from the cave taking only the sword with them. Along the shingle they ran all the while expecting to hear the sounds of pursuit. When they reached the shoal at the cliff Droplaug was exhausted, since she was in poor health following her stay in the cave, and Thorvald took her in his arms and carried her through the water. It was much deeper now since the tide was coming in and his progress was slow. As he approached the spur of rock he noticed a ledge carved out of the rock some way up the cliff. Now they heard a great roar from the cave and knew that they had been discovered. Looking at the moon and stars Thorvald realised that it was close to dawn and that they stood no chance of creeping away unseen. Droplaug begged him to leave her behind and save himself, but Thorvald would not hear of it.

He took off his cloak and put it around her and then he staggered to the ridge and placed her carefully in the cleft. "Our fates are entwined and as long as I can hold onto you we shall never be parted." So saying he turned to face the giant. The troll was so huge that Thorvald could clearly see his head and shoulders above the spur of rock. Then he realised the purpose of the ledge. Geiter had carved it to allow him to climb over the rock spur without getting his feet wet. Thorvald saw a chance and drawing the marvellous sword he ran forward. The giant put his foot on the ledge and swung his leg over the rock spur. As his foot came down onto the beach Thorvald sprang forward and swinging the sword with all his strength he cut clean through the giant's leg just above the knee. The giant fell with a thunderous noise and lay upon the sand his face a mask of agony. In his pain he cried out to Thorvald.

"You stole the only weapon which could do me harm. I did not think a puny human would be able to wield it and yet you have turned out to be the death of me. But I swear that the weapon will be for ever more cursed and it will be of little help to you when you need it most."

Thorvald stepped forward and struck the giant's neck so great a blow that his head sprang from his shoulders and rolled down the beach. Thorvald picked it up and placed it between the giant's thighs. Then he went to Droplaug and found that she had fainted through fear and exhaustion. He picked her up and wearily made his way back to the hall of her father where the household were just preparing breakfast. Some men had remarked his absence but thought nothing of it.

Thorvald entered the hall and he carried Droplaug in one arm and held the sword in the other. He presented himself to the Earl and said that he had brought him his daughter. Great was the joy of the Earl and all those assembled and Thorvald was made to recount the whole adventure.

Earl Bjorgolf said that he must be a fortunate man indeed to defeat such a monster on his own and many of the Earl's men spoke behind their hands and said that it could not have been such a monster after all perhaps. Thorvald turned to go back to his seat and the Earl called after him and bade him come sit on the front bench near the high seat. " You are either a man worthy of more honour than I have shown you or you are a lying dog who will live only until we can discover the truth of the matter. You have returned my daughter and that is a great gift but we will go shortly and see the truth of your tale."

So the Earl and his men finished their breakfast and, arming themselves, they set out for the spot that Thorvald had described. There they saw the monster's body and how it had been slain and they marvelled at the courage of the Icelander. The Earl's men who had mocked him were shamed and slunk away. Bjorgolf ordered that driftwood should be collected and a huge pyre was built where the body of the giant was burned to ashes and the ashes were scattered onto the sea.

Then they got their boats and went to the cave of the giant and found there a great deal of goods most of it of great value and they loaded it into their ships and transported it to the hall of the Earl. Since then those places have been called Geitishellir and Geitishamrar but no trolls have ever lived there again.

When all the goods were gathered much of it was recognised, including a great deal of Thorvald's own goods from the shipwreck. The Earl declared that those goods which had been identified should be given back to their owners and when this was done there was a great deal left over of which he gave full measure to Thorvald.

Thorvald then stayed in Shetland with great honour as what he had done was considered to be outstanding and worthy of great respect. He stayed for another full year with the Earl. Word of his deeds even reached Iceland and the people of the East Fjords were glad and they said that his good fortune was a repayment for the shabby way in which his brother had treated him. Hearing this Ketil was not pleased and he pretended to have no knowledge of his brother's feats.

Thorvald waited till the approach of another Yule and then went to speak to Bjorgolf. He reminded the Earl of his promise and asked if he could claim his bride. The Earl said that he could think of no better man to wed his daughter but that he feared Thorvald would get the worst of the bargain as her temperament had been less than good since her time with the giant. Thorvald answered that he was well aware of this but that she seemed to think well of him and he believed they would make a good match.

Bjorgolf then offered that Thorvald could rule in his place until his sons were old enough to take on their responsibilities but Thorvald said that it would be better for their father to continue his rule as he wished to return to Iceland and he did not think he was suited to rule men anyway.

Then Droplaug's mother was called to give her blessing to the match and they were betrothed. The Earl gave his daughter a large dowry and there was a magnificent wedding feast with all manner of food and drink and a great many important guests. At the end Thorvald gave his guests many fine presents and settled down with his new bride to await the spring. Their married life was happy and they treated each other well, although many people thought Droplaug to be too proud and cold.

In the spring Thorvald bought a ship and made ready to sail to Iceland. Droplaug's mother Arneid decided to sail with them and handed over her property to her sons. A man called Grim Hallernuson who had befriended Thorvald also went with them. They had favourable winds and landed in Iceland in early summer at a place called Hofn in Borgarfjord to the south of Njardvik. Many of Thorvald's kinsmen rode to the ship to greet him and all invited him and his companions to stay with them. But his brother did not come and Thorvald sent no word to him.

Thus ended Throvald's adventures in Shetland and although he and his family had many more they do not come into this story but can be found in the Saga of the People of Fljotdal.

VOYAGE OF THE DRATSIE

*A*t the end of the 15th Century Shetland was pledged as surety for the payment of a dowry owed to Scotland by Denmark. The kings of Scotland thereby gained rights on the islands but not sovereignty and the pledge assured that the islands would only be subject to the king himself or his direct heir. This situation continued for almost a century during which the king was represented by a variety of chamberlains until Mary Queen of Scots granted the islands to her half brother Lord Robert Stewart. The islands at that time were still subject to Norse law and this gave the udallers (freemen) of Shetland considerably more autonomy than their feudal equivalents on the Scottish mainland, an autonomy that they exercised quite freely. Robert Stewart then handed the islands over to his half brother Laurence Bruce of Cultmalindie to administer on his behalf and appointed him as Foud (Sheriff) of the islands and thus our story begins.*

Laurence Bruce was a man who had little time for law and rights and as soon as he was given control of the islands he set about squeezing the people of Shetland for every penny he could get out of them. He had brought his own soldiers with him from Perthshire and he used these to control the local population and to impose his new laws and taxes on the people. As always there were those locals who were willing to serve whoever was in power as long as the money was right and these were appointed as ranselmen and acted as tax collectors and constables.

Bruce used his forces well and began a reign of terror when no man was safe on his farm or of his possessions. People were dragged before his court on trumped up charges and their lands were forfeited to Bruce himself. The legitimate judicial system of the islands, operated through the Norse Alting, was ignored and the petitions of the leading udallers were met with scorn. Bruce even made it a capital offence to leave the islands and thus his offences were kept secret from the outside world.

Nowhere was his presence more keenly felt than on the island of Unst. Unst had been extensively settled by the Norsemen who had lived there for centuries and as freemen had established good farms and prosperous communities. Bruce chose to make his headquarters there

and built himself a castle at Muness in the south end of the island. From this stronghold he now began a concerted campaign to dispossess all these freemen and replace them with tenants who had pledged allegiance to him. Men and women who held land and houses were accused of sheep stealing, witchcraft and worse. The witnesses were inevitably called from amongst Bruce's ranselmen and the penalty always involved the confiscation of property and sometimes even the execution of the hapless victim.

It was against this background of fear and suspicion that the udallers of Unst met in secret conclave to discuss their situation. They readily acknowledged that it was pointless to approach Bruce with any hope of getting him to restore their rights and thus they were left to examine the alternatives. Open rebellion was a possibility suggested by many, these were after all the descendants of a warrior race, and there were few households that did not have a sword or axe hidden somewhere despite Bruce's laws which forbade their possession. The islanders were precious few to take on the might of someone of Bruce's stature and he could easily hire enough soldiers to wipe out the entire population of the island if he had a mind. Few doubted that he would happily do so if the opportunity presented itself and he could justify the massacre to his masters on the Scottish mainland. Then of course there was the castle, the storming of which would be no easy task for a few men armed with just swords and spears. The udallers of Unst valued their freedom but were pragmatic enough to accept that freedom isn't much good to you if you're dead. Others suggested that the best course of action would be to comply with the Foud and wait till he fell out of favour with the king or even his half brother Lord Robert, but many argued that it was likely that they would all be homeless or dead before that could happen so there was little hope in that course of action.

At the back of the room sat one of the older men, Thorburn of Dalsetter. Grey bearded yet still a vigorous man he listened to the arguments rumble backwards and forwards as first one and then another of those present went over the same ground time and time again. At last he stood up and walked forward into the firelight. The room fell silent as he looked around the assembly and all listened as he spoke.

"Only one man in Scotland has power to govern us and only one man has the power to save us from this serpent who sucks our life's blood. The law states that we are subject to none but the king and to the king we must go and lay our complaints."

His statement was greeted by stunned silence. The king was in far off Edinburgh and travel outside the islands was strictly forbidden. Even if anyone was brave enough to attempt the journey no ships left the islands that were not thoroughly searched by Bruce's men. The udallers considered all this and although many felt that a petition to the king might bring some results most felt that getting to him would be well nigh impossible.

Thorburn spoke once more "My ancestors sailed many miles to reach this spot and our forebears sailed a good deal further in search of lands where they could be free. I have a good boat, six oared and sound as any on these islands. I will sail to meet the king and bring him our petition if six others will sail with me."

Once more he looked around the room and many there could not meet his gaze. So many miles in an open boat could prove as dangerous as waiting for Bruce's men to call and for many the thought of fighting wind and waves was more frightening than fighting soldiers. Some still had the blood of the Vikings in their veins however and, after a moment's hesitation, six young men walked into the firelight and stood next to the old man.

It was decided that the expedition must leave quickly before Bruce got word of what was happening and the men who were to carry the message rushed home to throw together a few bits and pieces to take with them. Food and water were quickly obtained and carried over the hill to where the old man's boat, the Dratsie, was waiting in her noost. One of the more educated of the men sat down to pen the letter which was to be carried to the king and all of those present made their mark on the parchment. Then, with a few swift goodbyes, they pushed the boat off and began to row steadily southwards. As they disappeared into the gloom of the evening those standing on the shore paused for a moment to wonder if they would ever see their friends again.

As expected Laurence Bruce soon found out about the expedition but there was little he could do by then to stop it. The Dratsie was well to the south by now and even his swiftest ships would not be able to find her in the vast expanse of the North Sea. Neither could he send a messenger to the king himself because that would acknowledge that there was a problem with his governing of the islands. Better, he thought, to leave it. The chances were they would perish in the cold windswept waters on the way south and even if they did make it to Edinburgh the king was unlikely to listen to a group of uncouth barbarians. In the meantime he would spend his time preparing for their return.

Most of the men who had gone were beyond his reach. They were young men with a sense of adventure but no families or farms to tie them to the land. Thorburn was a different matter however and had one of the best farms on Unst and a grown up daughter both of whom would play their part in his vengeance for this impertinence. The farm was seized immediately and the girl was imprisoned in Muness Castle. Bruce had her locked in one of the upper rooms and after allowing her a little time to contemplate her fate he went to visit her. To his surprise the girl was both pretty and proud and when he saw and spoke to her a scheme began to take shape in his mind. His youngest son was as yet single and it seemed to Bruce that it would be both amusing and expedient to marry him off to this arrogant island beauty. As well as being a blow to the pride of the stiff-necked islanders it would help legitimise his seizure of the farm, especially if the old man did not survive his journey.

Thorburn's daughter Helga spent many a weary hour gazing from her room in the castle turret. She knew that escape was pointless until the return of her father. Even if she got out of the castle there was nowhere to run on the small island that was her home and no means to escape to the mainland either. So she spent her days scanning the southern horizon for some glimpse of a sail that might be a sign of her rescue. She had little doubt that her father would be successful in his petition and that he would return with word from the king himself. So it was that, from her high vantage point, she was among the first to spot a sail on the horizon coming from the south. It was approaching twilight on a late summers evening and the strong wind and vicious tides were whipping the sea into a maelstrom of waves and broken water. Unable to risk the tide race of Bluemull Sound the craft was steering for the east side of Unst hoping perhaps to be able to beach at the north end of the island. This course however meant they had to sail past the stronghold of Laurence Bruce and under the very eyes of the watchers he had placed on the castle walls. Helga began to tear up the sheets from her bed determined to make her escape and join her father.

Bruce was well prepared for the return of the Dratsie and soon he and his son Edwin collected a squad of men armed with pike and matchlock and set off to intercept the boat as soon as she came ashore. Regardless of what the outcome of their quest had been he reckoned that, if he could seize and imprison them immediately, no one else need ever learn of the crews' fate. The storm would act in his favour especially if the upturned boat was found drifting when it abated. He could then question the men and have them quietly strangled in the cellars of his castle before throwing their worthless carcasses into the sea. He led his men swiftly northwards guessing that the craft would make for Baltasound or even try to get as far as Norwick. The Boat was still well to the south and he stopped regularly to check its position and try to guess at its eventual destination. At one such halt he gazed backwards and to his chagrin he spotted that the Dratsie had dropped her sail and, cutting swiftly across the tide stream, was being rapidly rowed towards the shore just to the north of his own castle. Furious at being outsmarted he turned and headed back, driving his men before him.

He issued instructions to the chief of his ranselmen Robert Kennedy. "If any one of these scoundrels offers the least resistance he is to die on the spot. No mercy, kill them all if you must." A few deaths on the beach would not matter much one way or the other he reasoned. There would be no witnesses on such a night as this and in any event the men had effectively condemned themselves by leaving the island in defiance of his direct order. Bruce was profoundly surprised therefore when, coming over the top of the Vord Hill, he found himself gazing down onto the beach at Sand Wick which was crowded with people. Bruce and Helga had not been the only people to spot the Dratsie and men, women and children had streamed down from the houses of Colvadale, Framgord and Sand Wick itself. They had even been joined by people from as far afield as Uyeasound and Clivocast keen to hear news of the expedition to Edinburgh.

Bruce paused to consider his position but knew in his heart that he had no choice but to confront the returning voyagers. He would have preferred fewer witnesses it was true but he could still effect an arrest and silence the men before they had a chance to spread any information around. He had to act swiftly and therefore he strode boldly down through the gathering and placed himself directly before Thorburn.

"This time you have gone too far old man," he shouted to make himself heard over the wind and the noise of the people. " You have defied the orders of the king's own representative on these islands and you must stand ready to take the consequences."

"So be it" replied Thorburn with quiet dignity "but for how much longer you will be the king's representative is open to question. The king himself has ordered a commission to look into your rule of our islands and it is on its way as we speak. I have here a parchment under the seal and signature of the king himself which says that no man has the right to hinder his subjects to go where they will on their honest business. So, my Lord Bruce, you may do with me as you wish but have a care as to what those on the road behind me may find when they arrive."

Thorburn then thrust his hand into the breast of his jacket and strode forward to present the parchment to the Foud. Robert Kennedy, mindful of the instructions he had received, decided that this constituted resistance to the will of Lord Bruce and raising his matchlock he fired at almost point blank range. Red blossomed from the old man's chest as the matchlock ball struck his heart. He fell dead at the feet of his travelling companions the parchment still clutched in his outstretched hand. One of the fellow travellers, a young red headed giant called Rolf, bellowed in fury and grasping a whaling harpoon from the boat rushed at Kennedy and drove the spear clean through his body, killing him on the spot.

Bruce looked around him at the angry faces and realised his life hung in the balance. One wrong word or one false move and these peasants would fall on him like the sea wolves they were descended from. Ironically he was saved by the arrival of Helga who took in the scene at a glance and went to kneel beside her father's body. Her obvious grief subdued the anger in the crowd and Bruce stood quietly waiting for the group to disperse. Edwin walked slowly up to the body and removed the parchment from the old man's hand. Helga looked up and their eyes locked.

"I am deeply sorry for your loss lady but we need to know what the king has said." Helga nodded and Edwin unrolled the parchment and began to read. After a few moments he lifted his head and looked directly at Bruce. "It is as he said father. The king has appointed a commission. I would suggest we leave these people to mourn their dead and return to Muness to prepare for their arrival." He motioned to some of his men to pick up the body of Kennedy and set off back towards the castle. Bruce stood for a moment undecided and then feeling the cold hard stares of the islanders upon him he turned on his heel and strode off in pursuit.

Over the next few days Edwin spent a great deal of time thinking about the young woman he had seen kneeling above her father's body. He found every excuse to visit Dalsetter and it seemed that Helga shared his feelings. Although still deeply in mourning for her father she felt strangely comforted by Edwin's presence and was happy at the thought that they might build a future together. Several locals noted the growing relationship with unease and there were dark mutterings around many fires in the houses of Unst at the thought of a local girl being wedded or even bedded by a son of the hated Laurence Bruce.

The body of Thorburn lay for several days while the proper preparations were made for his burial. On the day of the funeral there was a strong wind blowing and heavy rain as the sad procession made its slow way to the burial ground. Edwin's presence was not appreciated by some of those in attendance and it was only out of respect for Thorburn that a fight did not break out at the funeral itself. Afterwards Edwin accompanied Helga home but most of the rest of the mourners repaired to a nearby house to drink to the dead man's memory.

Just after dark a loud knocking came to the door of Dalsetter and when Helga answered a young boy stood on the threshold, breathless and white faced. "My mother sent me to warn you mistress," he stammered, "Rolf is drunk and on his way here with like company and murder in his heart. Its you and the laird's son he has a mind to kill."

"How many?" asked Edwin. "A dozen or more" replied the boy, "and all armed. You must get away from here if you want to see the night out."

Edwin quickly took stock of their position. They couldn't risk making a dash southwards to Muness in case they stumbled upon Rolf and his companions. Likewise if they went north they were backing themselves into a corner and would be trapped like rats in a barrel. The strong winds made escape by sea risky but there seemed little alternative and they soon launched one of the smaller boats belonging to the farm intending to row southwards. What happened in the storm tossed tides of Bluemull sound can only be guessed at but the young couple never reached their destination nor were their bodies ever found. Perhaps their boat foundered in the heaving seas or just perhaps they reached Yell and made a life for themselves in some far off place many leagues from local prejudice.

Although Laurence Bruce's power was severely curtailed when his benefactor Lord Robert died and was succeeded by his son the infamous Earl Patrick the voyage of the Dratsie proved to be the last protest by the independent udallers in Shetland and signalled the start of a pervasive Scottish control of the islands. It was a final eloquent gesture towards an independence the islands were never to achieve again.

SOME RECOMMENDED READING FOR THE STUDENT OF SHETLAND'S VIKINGS AND FOLKLORE

The Folklore of Orkney and Shetland
Ernest W. Marwick – Birlinn Ltd
Possibly the definitive work on folklore in Orkney and Shetland and certainly a marvellous resource for anyone interested in this fascinating subject.

Orkneyinga Saga
Anonymous – Penguin Classics
The history of the Earls of Orkney and Shetland. A "must read" for those interested in the Viking period in both Orkney and Shetland.

Told Round the Peat Fire
Andrew T. Cluness – Shetland Publishing Company
An excellent collection of stories, both ancient and more recent, told by a master storyteller. Thoroughly enjoyable and heartily recommended.

Shetland Folklore
John Spence – Llanerch Press
A first class work with a great section on proverbs and sayings.

Orkney and Shetland Folklore
G. F. Black – Llanerch Press
More of a collection than a single work but full of interesting bits and pieces.

The Complete Sagas of Icelanders
Various – Leifur Eriksson Publishing
The newest and most complete translation of this considerable body of work. Beautifully produced and eminently readable it should be on every Viking devotee's bookshelf.

The work of Jamsie Laurenson is largely unpublished and can be found mostly through transcriptions of tapes, which he made for the School of Scottish Studies, and articles that he wrote for various magazines.

The above list is by no means exhaustive and is designed merely to entice the reader into further researches into this fascinating area. I wish you a very enjoyable journey.